The BROONS

Read all aboot them!

Now then, we've seen your choice in books,
You like The Broons, we know.
But whit dae a' THAT family read?
Well, tak' a look below . . .

You'll all have guessed that Daphne likes
Love stories and Romances.
But when she tak's the books back late,
She gets no loving glances!

The fitba' paper's Joe Broon's choice—
It's the scores he likes tae see.
But when the bairn gets it first—
They need a referee!

Their comics tell a tale or two
Of fighting through the ages.
But when the twins both want first read,
It's the Battle of the Pages!

To Gran'paw Broon, the cowboy fan,
Gunslinger books are braw.
And when he chugs upon his pipe,
He's Scotland's fastest draw!

Horace reads a lot, of course,
It's high-brow stuff for him.
But there's a time when even he
Thinks HEAVY books are grim!

But there's one read, the Broons agree
They all enjoy the most,
When on a Sunday morning
They gather round " The Post "!

Printed and published by D.C. Thomson & Co., Ltd., 185 Fleet Street, London EC4A 2HS.

Help ma boab! Whit a thought—

Gran'paw Broon as a curly-top!

Stripes and squiggles, fancy check—
The Broon lads catch it in the neck!

What is it about bins and brushes—

That brings poor Daphne oot in blushes?

Hen Broon really shouldn't boast—

When he gets a brand new "post"!

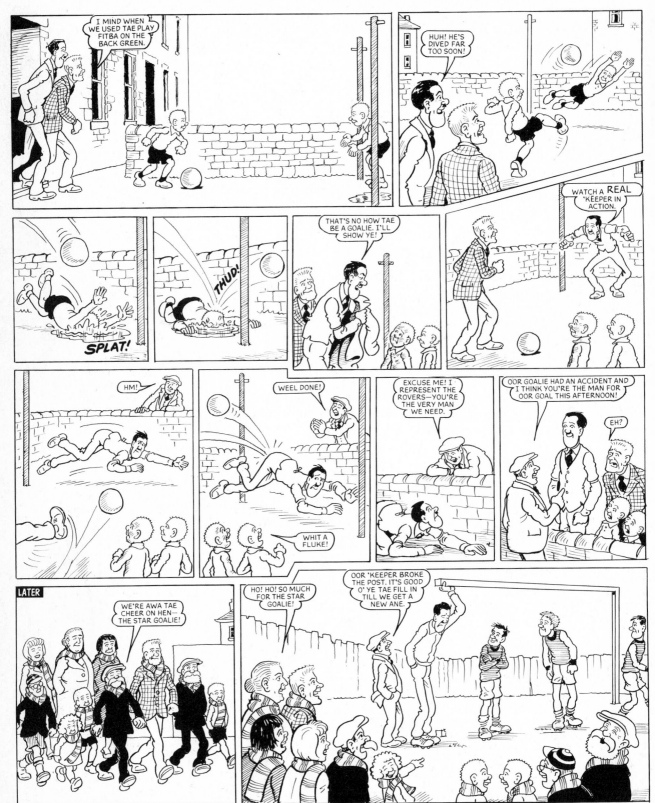

The sweetest granny in toon—

Upsets the youngest Broon!

Paw shows that he's no daft—

When he's troubled wi' a draught!

On Burns' Nicht the Broons all wish—

Tae sample Scotland's " national dish"!

Ye've met auld anes who are needy—

Now meet one who is speedy!

He's a busy lad is Paw—

But try tellin' that to Maw!

It's just no joke—

The day the brake broke!

OOR CARTIE'S BROKEN, PAW! WILL YOU SORT IT FOR US?

ACH, I'M TOO TIRED! I WANT TO SIT BY THE FIRE AND READ MY PAPER.

OH, JOHN MACKAY'S COMIN' OVER TO SEE YE FOR A COUPLE OF HOURS, PAW.

WHAT? THAT AULD WINDBAG!

HIS STORIES WOULD DRIVE YE ROUND THE BEND! I'M GETTIN' OOT! COME ON, YOU TWA—I'LL SORT YER CARTIE!

YE'LL FIND IT IN THE WASHIN' HOOSE. WE'RE AWA' FOR SOME SWEETS.

TWO HOURS LISTENIN' TO MACKAY! NOT ON YOUR LIFE! I'LL SOON HAVE THIS CARTIE MENDED, THEN I'LL READ MY PAPER TILL HE'S GONE!

THAT'S IT! IT'S JUST THE WHEELS THAT WERE LOOSE!

I WOULDN'T MIND A RUN ON IT MYSELF!

THERE'S NOBODY ABOOT! I'LL JUST HAVE A RUN DOON THE HILL—I COULD SAY I WAS TESTIN' IT FOR THE BAIRNS!

THERE'S THE MERRYGATE STEPS— I'D BETTER PUT THE BRAKE ON!

HELP! IT'S NOT WORKIN'!

BUMP!

BUMP!

LOOK OUT! I CAN'T STOP, MISTER! HELP!

BROON!

CRASH!

WE FORGOT TO TELL YE, PAW. THE BRAKE WAS BROKEN TOO!

OH, JINGS! IT'S YOU, MISTER MACKAY!

THEY'LL BE ALL RIGHT IN A COUPLE OF DAYS, MRS BROWN! JUST A BIT BRUISED!

A COUPLE O' DAYS! AND THIS ALL STARTED BECAUSE I WANTED TO DODGE HIM FOR A COUPLE O' HOURS!

CHEER UP, BROON! IT WAS AN ACCIDENT! NOW, DID I EVER TELL YE ABOOT THE TIME I WAS IN SOUTH AMERICA? THERE I WAS, SURROUNDED BY TWENTY THOUSAND SAVAGE PYGMIES— BLAH! BLAH! BLAH!—

DUDLEY D WATKINS

There's many a " Hen "—

At No. 10!

Gran'paw's taken aback—

By this noisy pack!

Ears are useful tae Paw Broon—

They stop his troosers fallin' doon!

Paw's got a nerve, the neighbours say—

But it's just his " feeling seedy " day!

For " peat's " sake—

What a mistake!

Doon the fog came—

And Paw " mist " his bus hame!

Paw Broon arranges—

Sweeping changes!

OH, DEAR, I JUST CANNA COPE WI' MY WORK LIKE I USED TO—IT'S TAKIN' ME LONGER EVERY DAY! I'M NEEDING A BREAK.

WE'LL NEED TAE GET A HOME HELP, PAW—YE'VE NO IDEA THE SWEEPIN' UP I'VE GOT TO DO. IT'S GETTING ME DOON.

WHIT? D'YE KEN WHIT IT COSTS TAE GET A HOME HELP? I'M NO' MADE O' MONEY!

ACH, MAYBE I'VE BEEN TOO HARD ON MAW. I'LL SEE IF I CAN GET SOMEBODY CHEAP TAE HELP HER OOT.

NEXT DAY

PIT THAT BROOM DOON, MAW! I'VE GOT IT A' ARRANGED—I'VE FIXED UP SOMEBODY TAE COME UP AN' DAE THE SWEEPIN' FOR YOU!

THAT'S RIGHT—YOU GO ROOND THE SHOPS, HAE A CUP O' COFFEE IN WILSON'S, ENJOY YERSEL'—I'LL SEE THE SWEEPIN'S DONE!

THAT'S REAL NICE O' YE, PAW!

OH, MRS TWEETIE—I HAVENA SEEN YE FOR AGES AND I'VE A KNITTIN' PATTERN I'VE BEEN WANTIN' TO GIE YE. WHY NO' COME UP FOR IT NOW...?

WELL, ER, YES, OF COURSE!

WE'LL HAVE A CUP O' COFFEE. I'LL GET MY—ER—HOME HELP TAE PUT ON THE KETTLE.

MMM!

HELLO, MRS BROON. BE FINISHED IN A MINUTE. SIT YERSEL' DOON!

OH!

Maw Broon's close is clean and bright—

But still Paw mak's the stairs pure white!

What a to-do—

Wi' the Broons at the zoo!

As a wrestler, Paw Broon's bad—

He's soon on the " deck", poor lad!

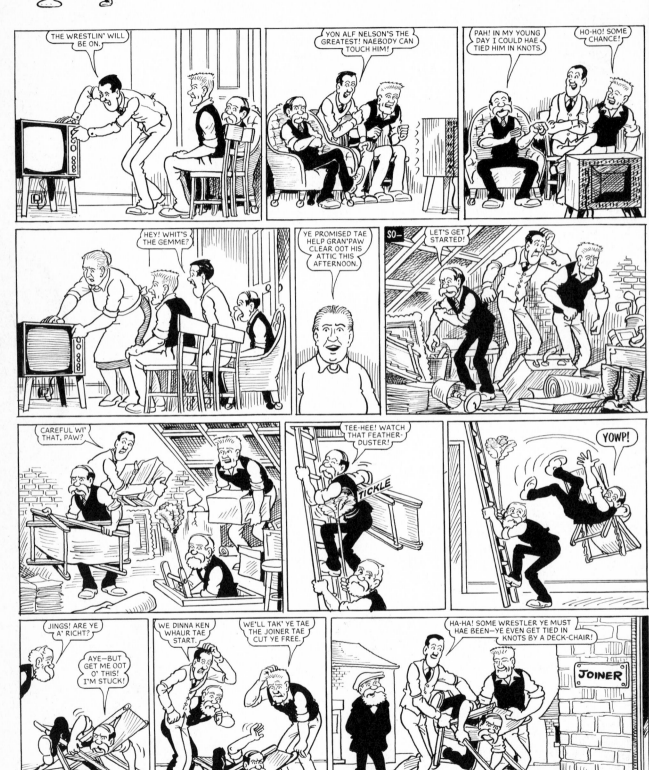

This weatherman's tip—

Mak's Paw feel a drip!

You'll get a hoot—

At Joe's " new " suit!

It's a night oot for Paw—

But what aboot Maw?

Maw gets a fright—

From this " stag "-gering sight!

It's a dog's life, they find—

When they try tae be kind!

Gran'paw causes distress—

Then, oh, what a mess!

Just for Maw's sake—

The Broons take a break!

Gran'paw's up tae tricks, but then—

There's another " big bairn " at No. 10!

Paw's a juggler! In fact—

He's hot stuff at this act!

It's enough tae mak' them SHED a tear—

G.P.'s mistake has cost them dear!

To the pictures they go—

But only ONE sees the show!

It's no' FAIR on the rest—

But the auld anes know best!

When there's work to be done—

It's time to run!

Maw's trolley's filled for free—

On this funny shopping spree!

This sounds like a real disaster—

Gran'paw wi' his arm in plaster!

Bairns like milk, that's true enough—

But this wee one drinks pints o' the stuff!

Gran'paw maybe looks a mess—

But it's the ' smartest ' way to dress!

By day this lad won't talk at all—

But at night he's on the ball!

These shoes are a painful pair—

But it's Daphne's HEAD that's sair!

Paw's a proper fly wee joker—

Come and meet his heavy ' smoker '!

This patchy time for Maw—

Is soon ' enjoyed ' by one an a'!

Paw and Maw have eyesight trouble—

When they think they're seeing double!

These golfers both are feeling green—

In the ' baggiest ' clothes you've seen!

Paw and Gran'paw are stuck for words—

There's scarce a cheep from those early birds!

Paw starts acting shirty when—

He sees a lassie cuddling Hen!

The wee bairn mak's her Paw so mad—

He's foaming at the mooth, poor lad!

Grand new styles for Maw Broon's hair—

From London, Paris and doon the stair!

This new hoose has the best—

But the Broons' hoose has the 'rest'!

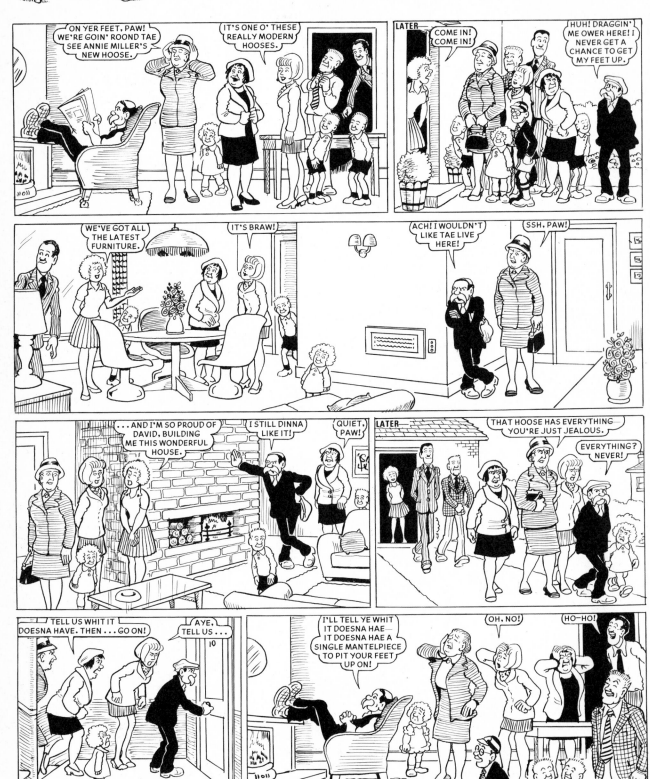

The funniest sight in a' the toon—

The one and only web-footed Broon!

Paw's not picked a thing up wrong—

But will his record last for long?

The family can't believe their eyes—

When they see Hen's ' big ' surprise!

There's not a cloud above the toon—

And yet the water buckets doon!

Is Daphne slimming? Surely no'—
This exercise has made her grow!

Dressin' up dogs makes Paw Broon frown—

But he soon gets a DRESSIN' down!

MEET LULU, PAW. SHE'S MY PAL'S PEKE. I'M LOOKING AFTER HER FOR A FEW DAYS!

JINGS! WHAT A CISSIE! WHO PUT THAT RIBBON ROUND HER NECK?

WHAT NEXT? A BATH IN FRONT O' THE FIRE? AND EXPENSIVE BATH SALTS, TOO!

HELP! A SHAMPOO, NOW—

—AND THE HAIR-DRIER! SURE YE DON'T WANT THE TOOTHPASTE?

NEXT DAY

DOGGIE HAIRDRESSING SALON

SHAMPOOS MANICURES PERMS

YE-YE-YE SURELY HAVEN'T BEEN IN THERE!

AYE! LULU WAS GETTIN' HER MANICURE. AN' IT'S NONE O' YOUR BUSINESS ANYWAY!

COME ON, PAW! ON YOUR FEET! WE SAID WE'D GIVE TAM MUNRO A HAND.

JINGS! I NEARLY FORGOT!

SCENT

LATER

PUT HER DOON, MAGGIE! THE WEE PET WILL LIKE A WALK IN THE COUNTRY.

HEY, DAPHNE—THERE'S AULD MUNRO'S PLACE—LET'S SEE IF PAW'S READY TO COME HOME YET.

THEY'RE ALL IN THE BARN, MRS BROON. JUST GO ON IN.

THAT'S BRAW!

WELL! LOOK WHAT HE'S UP TO! AFTER ALL HE SAID. HO-HO!

MAW!

GRAND HORSE SHOW at KILLIEBURNIE Saturday First

THAT'S WHO WAS LAUGHIN' AT US DOLLIN' UP LULU!

DUDLEY D. WATKINS

See poor Paw make—

A bad ' mis-steak '!

Maw Broon thinks she's having fun—

But a woman's work is never done!

The Broons can hardly wait—

To meet G.P.'s new ' date '!

OKAY, GRAN'PAW! YE CAN HAVE THE BATHROOM NOW!

THANKS, LAD. I'M NEEDIN' A WASH AN' BRUSH UP.

MY—GRAN'PAW'S HAVIN' A WASH! MUST BE SOMETHIN' SPECIAL ON!

WAROOOGHH! VERY FUNNY! I'M HAVIN' A NIGHT OOT, THAT'S ALL! SLOOOSSH!

DID YE GET THE SCISSORS, LASS?

AYE, GRAN'PAW— HERE YE ARE!

HE'S GOING TO TRIM HIS BEARD, MAGGIE—I THINK HE'S GOT A DATE TONIGHT!

WHO— HIM?

JINGS! HORACE'S HAIR-CREAM! IT MUST BE A SPECIAL DO! WHERE ARE YE GOIN'?

I'M TAKIN' MY LASS TO THE PICTURES—BEST SEATS AN' A BOX O' CHOCOLATES.

YOUR.LASS!

I'LL BET IT'S AGGIE MACGREGOR—SHE'S ALWAYS BEEN AFTER GRAN'PAW! KNITS HIM SOCKS EVERY WINTER!

AYE—HE TAKES THE SOCKS—BUT REFUSES HER! MAYBE HE'S SOFTENIN' AT LAST!

OR ELSE IT'S BIG FLORA! SHE'S FOREVER COOKIN' BRAW PASTRIES AN' THINGS FOR GRAN'PAW! SHE'S MAYBE HOOKED HIM WI' A PIE AT LAST!

COME ON, YE AULD ROMEO! TELL US! WHO IS IT?

HERE SHE IS NOW!

OKAY, GRAN'PAW! SHE'S READY! OFF YE GO!

THE BAIRN!

The firemen see red—

When Paw uses his head!

Maw would be the talk o' the town—

If she went dancing in THIS gown!

Hen and Joe get a fright—
From a very ' fishy ' sight!

Help m' boab! You'll laugh to see—

The Bairn's very own G.P.!

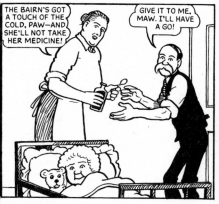

You just can't take a loan of Maw—

She knows how to HANDLE Paw!

Guess who makes a fuss—

On the "No. 10" bus.

He thinks he's smart, but wait a minute—

Paw Broon's put his foot right in it!

The family all change their tunes—

When they meet the other " Broons "!

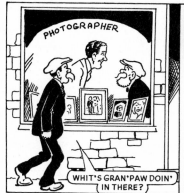

This horseplay by Paw—

Means a " run-in " wi' the Law!

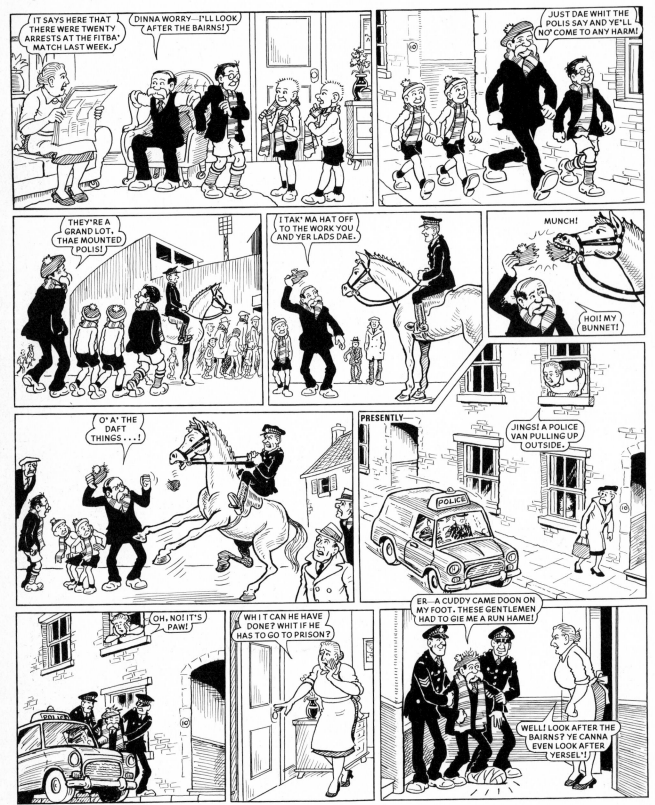

A funny sight that's hard tae beat—

It's raining tatties in Glebe Street.

The Long Johns he tries—

Cut Paw doon tae size!

Half o' him's Polish, half o' him's French—

And Daphne Broon is his new wench!

JINGS! LOOK! THERE'S OOR DAPHNE WITH A NEW LAD!

THAT ONE MUST BE RICH! HE'S GOT HIS OWN SHOP!

WE'RE GOIN' TO THE CINEMA, THEN I'M BRINGIN' HIM UP TO THE HOOSE FOR SUPPER! YOU RUN HOME NOW AND TELL MAW TO EXPECT US.

ME TELL MAW!

WHISPER— NOW—ALL TOGETHER— ONE—TWO—THREE—

DAPHNE'S BRINGIN' HER NEW LAD IN TO SUPPER! AND HE'S A FOREIGNER—HALF POLISH AND HALF FRENCH!

WHAT? AND MAW AWAY OUT?

WHAT'LL WE HAVE?

FISH AN' CHIPS?

NO! NO! WE'LL HAVE TO LOOK UP A FOREIGN RECIPE!

HE HAS A SHOP IN BELL STREET.

HERE'S THESE TWO OLD FLAGS OOT O' THE HALL CUPBOARD—FROM FRANCE AND POLAND.

I'LL MAKE UP A FRENCH SALAD!

WE'VE BEEN TO THE STOBIE POND AN' GOT FROGS AN' SNAILS! THAT'S WHAT FRENCHIES EAT.

DON'T BE DAFT!

D'YE KNOW THE LAD'S NAME?

AYE! IT'S ANGUS McKAY!

WHAT? I'VE NEVER HEARD O' A FOREIGNER WITH A NAME LIKE McKAY!

IT'S RIGHT ENOUGH! HE'S HALF POLISH AND HALF FRENCH! YOU COME DOON TO BELL STREET AN' WE'LL PROVE IT!

ARE YE SURE IT'S NOT SOME NAME LIKE MARCEL OR WALESKI?

OR PIERRE OR GASTON?

YOU'LL SOON SEE!

THERE YE ARE—WHAT DID I TELL YE!

ANGUS McKAY
FRENCH POLISHER

YE SILLY ASSES! A FRENCH POLISHER'S A MAN THAT POLISHES FURNITURE!

JINGS! NO KIDDIN'

No wonder Paw is looking grim—

His past is catching up with him!

Is an arrow from Cupid—

Making Gran'paw act stupid?

For once the family all agree—

This boyfriend suits Daph to a " T "!

Paw and Gran'paw go astray—

But still get HOSPITALity!

Maw thinks her hubby is no dunce—

She feels he's used his LOAF for once!

WELL, THAT'S MAW'S BREAD BOUGHT, GRAN'PAW. WE CAN GO HOME NOW!

FARTHER ON

HELP M'BOAB! I'VE JUST REMEMBERED—IT WAS SLICED BREAD MAW WANTED.

ACH! I'M NOT WALKIN' AWA' BACK THERE ON MY AULD LEGS. HERE, COME INTO TAM'S. HE'LL FIX US UP.

HEY, TAM! WHAT ABOOT SLICIN' THIS LOAF ON YER BACON SLICER TO SAVE US GOIN' AWA' BACK TO THE BAKERS?

SURE! HAND IT OVER!

HELP! TAM! WHOA! THAT'S FAR TOO THIN! IT'S NOT BACON YE'RE SLICIN'!

HOW'S THAT?

NO, NO! THAT'S FAR TOO THICK NOW! IT'S NOT GREAT THICK DOORSTEPS WE WANT!

THAT BETTER?

AYE, THAT'S MORE LIKE IT!

YOU AN' YER BRIGHT IDEAS! WHAT'S MAW GOIN' TO SAY NOW? ALL DIFFERENT SIZES O' SLICES! SHE'LL KNOW FINE WE DIDN'T GET IT THAT WAY!

ACH! I WAS ONLY TRYIN' TO HELP YOU!

OH-ER-HERE'S YER-ER-BREAD, MAW—SLICED, JUST LIKE YE-ER-ASKED FOR!

THANKS, PAW!

MY, THIS IS WONDERFUL!

WONDERFUL?

IT'S A WONDER NOBODY THOUGHT O' THIS BEFORE! WEE DAINTY SLICES FOR THE LASSIES—BIG DOORSTEPS FOR THE WEANS AND GRAN'PAW—AND ORDINARY ONES FOR THE REST O' US! YE'LL HAVE TO GET ONE O' THOSE LOAVES AGAIN NEXT TIME, PAW.

OH-ER-SURE, MAW. I'LL-ER-TRY, MAW!

This " dicky bird "—

Is quite absurd!

Gran'paw's smart, but there's a catch—

He's well and truly met his match!

Paw's forty winks lead to disaster!—

He wakens up to falling plaster!

Paw knows where to go—

To take a RISE out of Joe!

They need a new couch, agree one an' a'—

But the big question is, will Paw go '' sofa ''?

One o' Maw's tricks—

Puts Paw in a fix!

Maw's got a pipe for Paw—

That he canna suck nor blaw!

Paw's out o' luck—

When a drawer comes unstuck!

It's a sad, sad day for Gran'paw Broon—

When he gets a seat, he CAN'T sit doon!

Gran'paw seems down on his luck—

But you-know-who won't see him stuck!

The Broons folk aren't rich, but golly—

You can't say Paw's not got the lolly!

The family's noisy, that's a fact—

So poor Paw reads the QUIET act!

This baby's far from happy—

With the way Joe ties a nappy!

He's got his ticket for the draw—

But then there is a BLOW for Paw!

Look below! The sight is weird—

Gran'paw's gone and changed his beard!

Maw Broon's pudding's no' as planned—

When this wee " charmer " lends a hand!

It's an awfy shock tae greet—

A first-foot wi' ower many feet!